Hiya Frankie

Beth and I hope you enjoy this story.
Just the first of many we hope to read to you
over the years.

Lots of love
Grandad and Beth xx

Susannah Shane • Britta Teckentrup

When I Became Your Grandad

nosy crow

When I became your grandad,
my heart filled with joy and pride.

And life is an adventure
now I have you by my side.

I'll tell you my best stories,
and you'll show me all your tricks.

And when we are together,
there's no problem we can't fix.

I love to watch the world go by
with you, my little one.

But playing all our games
is still my favourite kind of fun.

When you are feeling gloomy
and the sky looks rather grey . . .

. . . I'll show you how a rainbow
brightens up the darkest day.

I love to think of all the things
your future has in store.

I know the world will listen
when you learn to use your roar!

So when you're feeling sleepy
and the moon is shining bright,

just know that Grandad loves you . . .

. . . and will always hold you tight.

For Grandpa John xx
S.S.

For Rolf-Arne
B.T.

First published 2022 by Nosy Crow Ltd
The Crow's Nest, 14 Baden Place
Crosby Row, London SE1 1YW
Nosy Crow Eireann Ltd, 44 Orchard Grove
Kenmare, Co Kerry V93 FY22, Ireland
www.nosycrow.com

ISBN 978 1 83994 445 1

Nosy Crow and associated logos are trademarks
and/or registered trademarks of Nosy Crow Ltd

Text by Susannah Shane
Text © Nosy Crow 2022
Illustrations © Britta Teckentrup 2022

The right of Susannah Shane to be identified as the author and
Britta Teckentrup to be identified as the illustrator of this work has been asserted.

A CIP catalogue record for this book is available from the British Library.

Printed in China
Papers used by Nosy Crow are made from
wood grown in sustainable forests.

10 9 8 7 6 5 4 3 2 1